CREATIVE GROWTH WITH

# HANDWRITING

Second Edition

**with the new Skill-Guide™ program**

**Book 2** O

### WALTER B. BARBE
Ph.D.; Editor-in-Chief, *Highlights for Children*;
Adjunct Professor, The Ohio State University

### VIRGINIA H. LUCAS
Ph.D.; Assistant Professor, Wittenberg University

### CLINTON S. HACKNEY
M.A.; Penman;
Consultant, Zaner-Bloser, Inc.

### CONSTANCE McALLISTER
Writer and Elementary School Teacher

Zaner-Bloser, Inc., Columbus, Ohio

# I Asked a Tiger to Tea

by Ivy O. Eastwick

I asked a tiger to tea;
he said
he would come
if he could;
but he had to visit
a very old aunt
who lived in Crabapple Wood.

I asked a giraffe to tea;
but he said
that he was
not able;
his neck made it
rather difficult
to eat from a dining table.

I asked a lion to tea;
but he said
that he just
couldn't bother . . .
so I think I will share
my afternoon tea
with my cat
and my dog
and my brother.

2

# PRE-TEST

## Self-evaluation

| | | yes | no |
|---|---|---|---|
| 1. | All my letters rest on the baseline. | ☐ | ☐ |
| 2. | My small letters touch the midline. | ☐ | ☐ |
| 3. | My middle-size letter *t* begins halfway between the headline and midline. | ☐ | ☐ |
| 4. | My tall letters touch the headline. | ☐ | ☐ |
| 5. | I have left a one-finger space between every word. | ☐ | ☐ |

l i t          o c a e

r m n u s

d f h b

v w k x z

g y p j q

LEFT-HANDED

RIGHT-HANDED

4

# LONG VOWEL SOUNDS

A long vowel sounds like the name of the letter. Say aloud these pictured words. Listen for the long sound of **a, e, i, o, u.** Write each of the words in lower-case letters and underline the long vowel.

A

E

I

O

U

cake

jeep

five

crow

cube

Write the invitation on practice paper.
Address your envelope here.

Come to a Zoo Party.
Where? Room _____
When? _____ , 19 ___
From _____

22

Z Z

P P

# Peanut Butter Kisses

Two cups dry milk
One cup peanut butter
One-half cup honey
One-fourth cup coconut

Write the ingredients below.

In a 2-quart bowl, mix dry milk,
peanut butter, and honey.
Roll dough into balls.
Roll the balls in coconut.
(Makes about 24 kisses.)

23

| The funny fish | My mittens | The best bunny |
|---|---|---|
| jumped over | gave me | ate |
| a pumpkin pie. | two tables. | a hot house. |

**GAMES**

For a party game, make cards on colored paper like the ones at the top of the page. Two people play.

Spread the papers upside down on the table. Each person picks one red paper, one blue paper, and one green paper. Put them together into a sentence. Put the upper-case letter first. Put the period at the end.

Take turns reading the sentences.

Which letters have at least one horizontal line?
Which letters have at least one vertical line? Slant line?

_____

_____

_____

_____

_____

_____

Write the lower-case letters that have circles or
parts of circles made clockwise.

_____

_____

_____

Seven upper-case letters have other letters in them.
Write the seven letters.

_____

_____

_____

_____

_____

# WHAT'S WRONG?

List what's wrong on practice paper.

26

# WRITE A THANK-YOU NOTE:
Some words to use:   Mr.   Miss   Ms.

party   Dear   Mrs.

_____

_____

_____

_____

_____

_____

_____

_____

_____

_____

_____

_____

_____

# CHANGING SOUNDS

Write each of these words.

1. cap

2. bit

3. hop

4. tub

Write each word again, but this time add a final **e**.

1.

2.

3.

4.

 a  e  i  o 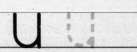 u

28

q g g

r r n n

p p

b b d d

Q Q                          Z z

Answer these
questions.

# SAFETY QUIZ

1. Why do schools have safety patrols?
2. Why do we have fire drills at school?
3. What is the first thing to do if there is an accident at school?
4. Is the sign "school" put on the street to tell children where to go?

# SAFETY AT SCHOOL

careful    accidents    hall

safety    slip    walk

stairs    danger

Write about safety.

Be careful with matches.

Cross the street at the corner.

Write your own safety slogans.

Stop, look, and listen
Before you cross the street.
Use your eyes and use
your ears
Before you use your feet.

33

1. Sunday

2. Monday

3. Tuesday     y y

4. Wednesday

5. Thursday

6. Friday    7. Saturday

1. What day comes before Saturday?
2. On what day does the Sunday paper come?
3. What day is Thanksgiving Day?
4. What is the first day of the school week?
5. What day comes after Monday?
6. What is the first day of the weekend?
7. What day have you still not listed?

1.

2.

3.

4.

36

5.

6.

7.

M M

T T

S S

W W

F F

Write words that rhyme
with each of these.

day

sun

tree

light

lake

**RHYMING WORD FAMILIES**

# TWO LINE RHYMES

_____

_____

_____

_____

_____

_____

_____

_____

_____

_____

_____

# THE FALL BREEZE

When I go a-walking,
I hear all the leaves rustling.
I feel the cool autumn breeze,
When I go a-walking.

Write a poem.

Aaron Herschman, Age 7
Bethany, Conn.

cold white
snowball ice
house wind
around sled

Write about winter.

41

# SPRING

I often sit and wonder why
The sky is always blue,
And all the robins sing their songs
When the spring is new.

Elizabeth Boese, Age 7
Redlands, Calif.

Write a poem.

42

Magnum Photos (Stock)

Magnum Photos (Burri)

picnic    watermelon

camping    swimming

sandwich    mosquito

Write about summer.

J J A A

In what month might you be doing these things?

1.

2.

3.

4.

March                    February

January April

44

# SCRAMBLED MONTHS

1. What month has only three letters in it?
2. What is the first month in summer?
3. What month beginning with **J** follows a month beginning with **J**?
4. What is the last full month of summer?

1. _____

2. _____

3. _____

4. _____

August    June    May    July

# SCRAMBLED MONTHS

O O

D D    N N

November    September    December    October

3.

2.

4.

1.

1. _____

2. _____

3. _____

4. _____

46

**WRITE YOUR CALENDAR**

| Sun. | Mon. | Tues. | Wed. | Thurs. | Fri. | Sat. |
|------|------|-------|------|--------|------|------|
|      |      |       |      |        |      |      |
|      |      |       |      |        |      |      |
|      |      |       |      |        |      |      |
|      |      |       |      |        |      |      |
|      |      |       |      |        |      |      |
|      |      |       |      |        |      |      |

Thirty days have September, April, June and November.
All the rest have 31 except February,
To which we 28 assign
Till Leap Year gives it 29.

1 2 3 4 5 6 7 8 9 0

47

How many things can you find
in this picture that begin with
the letter **s?**

S

aprilshowersbringmayflowers

p   p

f   f

w   w

l   l

49

It works! Pet shops sell a special collar that kills fleas. There is a rope kind that ties around the dog's or cat's neck, and also a plastic buckle kind which ties around its neck. Most people wonder why it goes around the neck.

Here is why. If a cat or dog goes outside in the summer, he will collect fleas. Fleas move very fast. They will probably run up the cat's neck. The fleas don't like the smell of the chemicals in the collar. The smell kills the fleas, and they drop off the cat or dog. So that's why you should buy a flea collar.

Kitty Kreitner, Age 8
Honesdale, Pa.

Describe something you know about.

_____

_____

**TITLE:** _____

_____

_____

_____

_____

_____

50 _____

51

# UPPER-CASE LETTERS
## FRIENDSHIP

How many words can you make from the letters in the above word? Write your words with upper-case letters.

1. PIN

2.

3.

4.

5.

6.

7.

8.

R          P          H

# BLENDING LETTERS

Write a word that goes with each picture.

broom

block

B B

# WHAT THE KING WANTED

If you were a king what would you want?

_____
_____
_____
_____
_____
_____
_____
_____
_____

K K k k

1. What did the King have?
2. Write one thing the King wanted.
3. Do kings know just what they want?

1.

2.

3.

plane
yes

cat
puppy

no
nothing

boat
pig

55

# MAKE THEM COME ALIVE

bed         bee

Change one letter to make these words come alive.

ax

jug

fist

X          j          b

56

# Words That Rhyme

Write at least four words
that rhyme with each of the pairs below.

_____  _____  _____

_____  _____  _____

_____  _____  _____

_____  _____  _____

_____  _____  _____

_____  _____  _____

_____  _____  _____

ran          spill          hat
tan          hill           sat

57

s s

es es

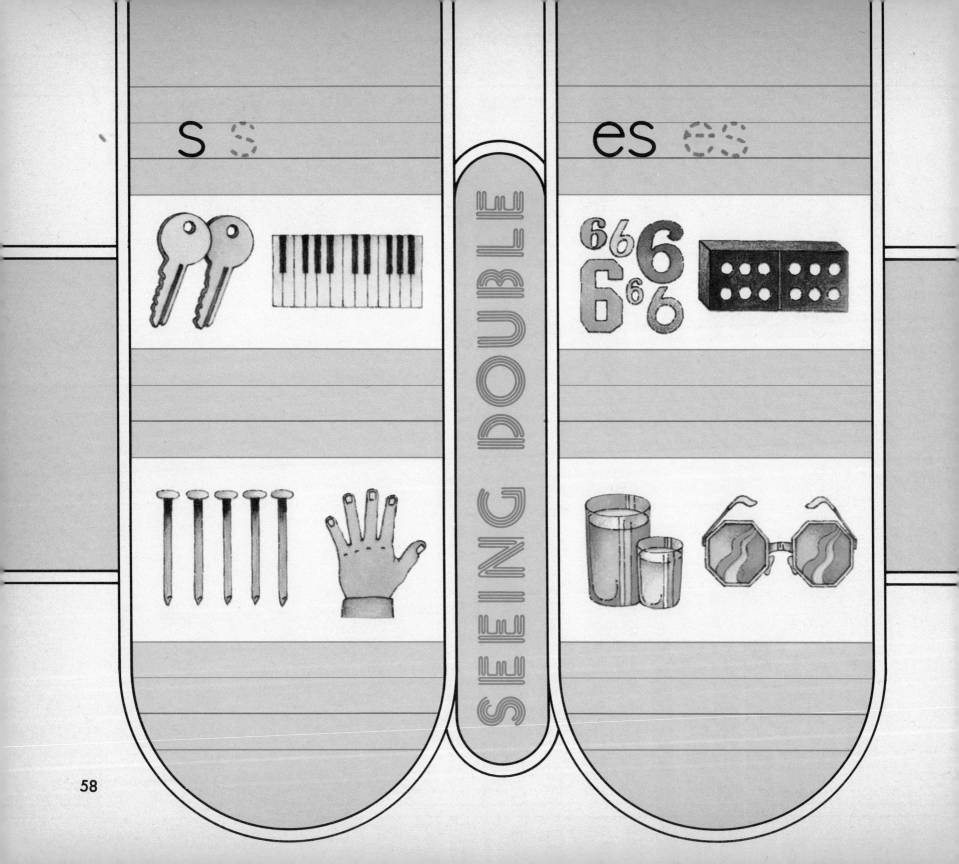

SEEING DOUBLE

58

Add **ed** and **ing** to each root word.

walk walked walking

pour

ask

kick

mow

ed _ed_ ing _ing_

59

A B C D

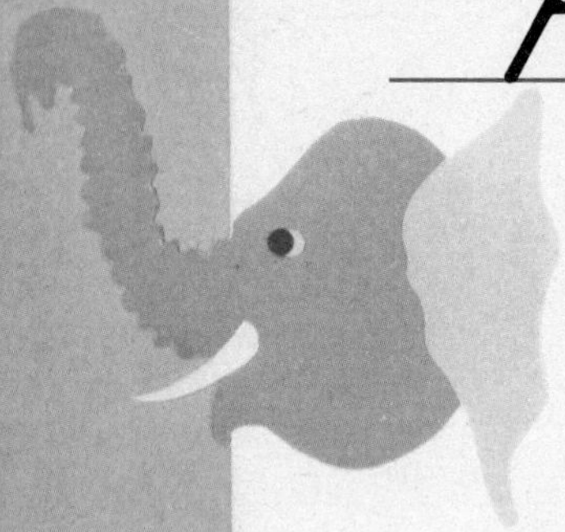

E F G H

I J K L

M N O

P Q R

S T U V

W X Y Z

60

a   b 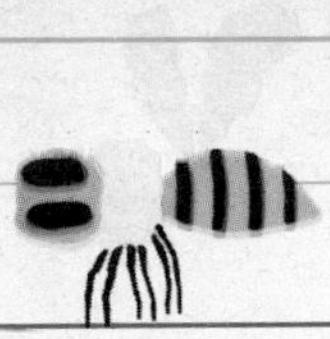   c   d

e    f   g   h

i   j   k   l

m   n   o   p

q   r    s   t

u   v   w

x   y   z

61

Write sentences with correct
# PUNCTUATION!

Did you see the lion

Mother said Come here

Bill yelled Stop

? ?   " "   ! !
. ,  .  .

# REVIEW

**1.** Write the straight line letters, upper and lower-case.

**2.** Write lower-case circle letters.

**3.** Write upper and lower-case slant letters.

**4.** Write lower-case tail letters.

# "OOPS!"

Someone is making a mistake. Write a sentence telling what the mistake is.

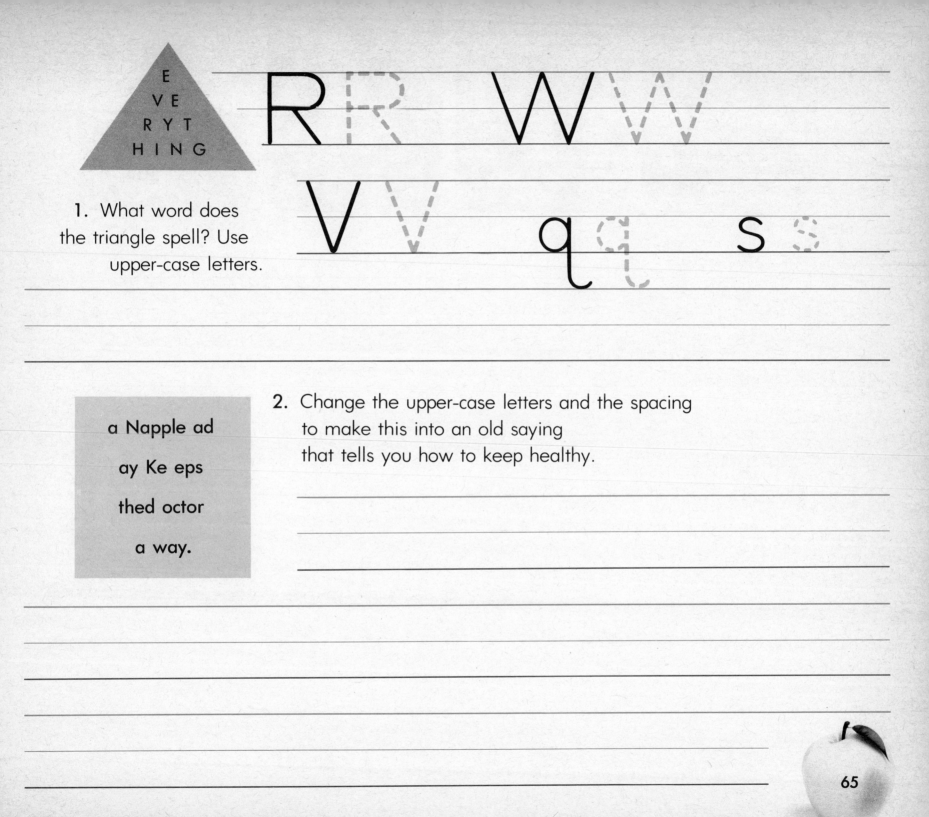

Rr Ww Vv q s s

**1.** What word does the triangle spell? Use upper-case letters.

a Napple ad

ay Ke eps

thed octor

a way.

**2.** Change the upper-case letters and the spacing to make this into an old saying that tells you how to keep healthy.

65

Write what is happening in this story.

_____

_____

_____

_____

_____

_____

_____

_____

_____

_____

_____

_____

_____

_____

_____

_____

_____

_____

fit a I in lock.
should turn I about.
If turn I, come you in.
not If, stay you out.

**UNSCRAMBLE EACH LINE**

67

# FINISH THE STORY

One day the wind saw a little red box lying in the road. "Oho!" said the wind. "I'll have some fun with that little box." So the wind puffed and blew and pushed that little red box down the rocky road. Bumpity-bump, thumpity-thump, it tumbled along. "Ouch!" said a voice from inside the box.

"I am sorry," said the wind. "I didn't know anyone was in there."

"Please help me out," said the tiny voice.

"I can't," said the wind. "I must hurry on and blow the weathervane so people will know where I am." And he blew away. Just then a brown-and-white dog came trotting down the rocky road.

Write the missing word.
Draw in the picture.

You sit 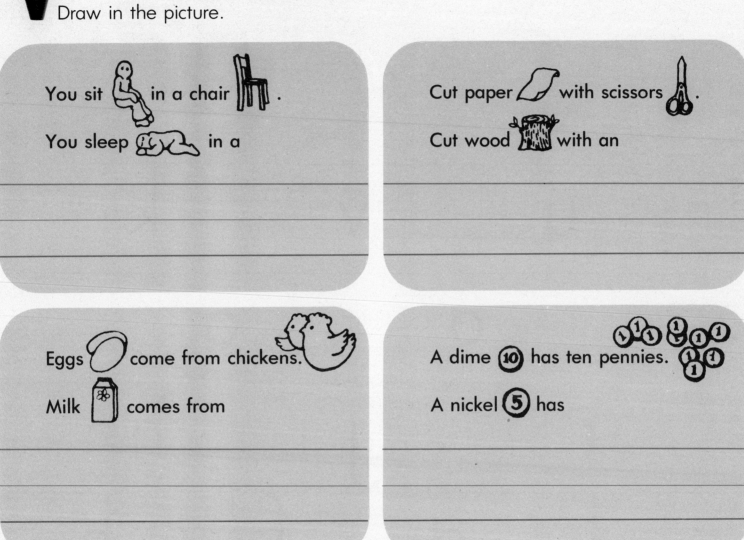 in a chair .

You sleep in a _____

_____

Cut paper with scissors .

Cut wood with an _____

_____

Eggs come from chickens.

Milk comes from _____

_____

A dime 10 has ten pennies.

A nickel 5 has _____

_____

X  X  e  e  W  W  V  V  i

# In my grandfather's trunk I found...

t        u        v        k

w        o        q

i        r        j        n

p        l        a        f        h

c        b        d        g

70

**1.**
Why is it hard to talk to a goat?

Choose and write the correct answer.

1.

**2.**
If your dog is lost, why don't you put an ad in the paper?

"My dog can't read."
"He always butts in."

2.

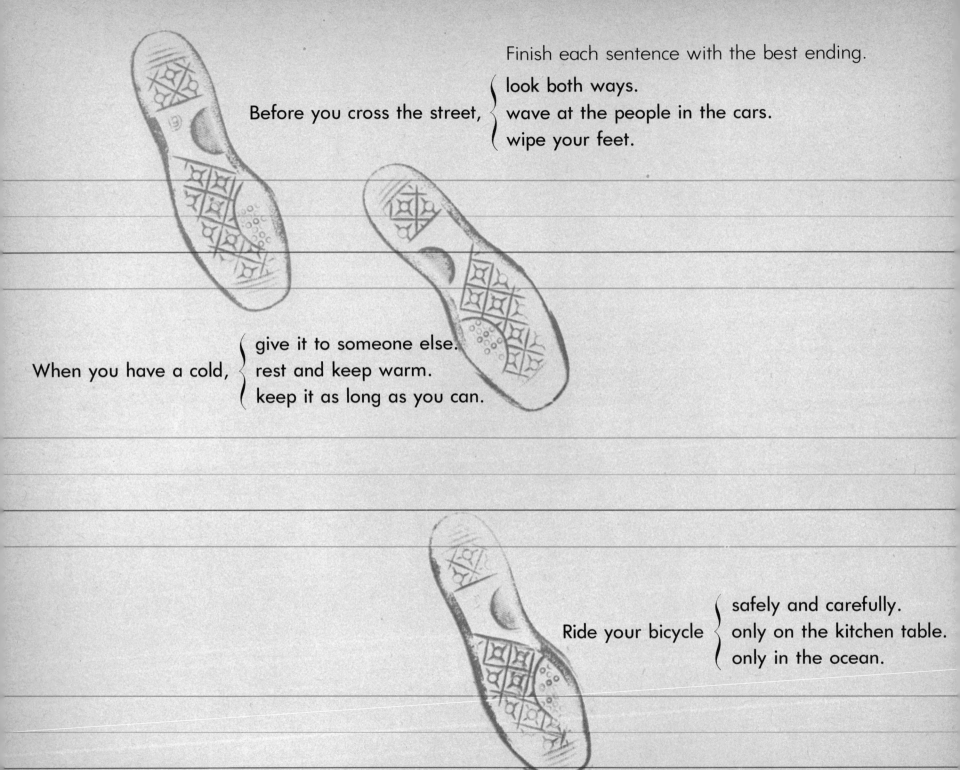

Finish each sentence with the best ending.

Before you cross the street,
- look both ways.
- wave at the people in the cars.
- wipe your feet.

When you have a cold,
- give it to someone else.
- rest and keep warm.
- keep it as long as you can.

Ride your bicycle
- safely and carefully.
- only on the kitchen table.
- only in the ocean.

## MYSTERY ANIMAL

The alphabet goes from a to z.
What animal goes from z to a?

# PUZZLE FUN:

z z r r

**1.**

**2.** Finish the magic square so it has every number from 1 to 9 in it, and so that every row across and every row down adds up to 15.

| 8 | 1 |   |
|---|---|---|
|   |   | 7 |
| 4 |   |   |

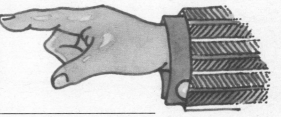

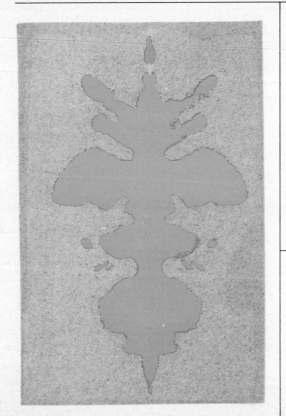

**3.** What picture do you see in the design? Write what you see on paper of your own.

## •HARDWARE•

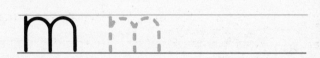

m m

## •TOYS•

How many things can you find in these pictures that begin with **m**? List them.

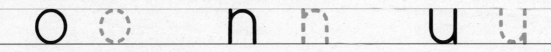

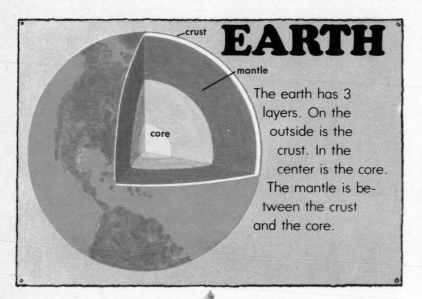

# EARTH

crust

mantle

core

The earth has 3 layers. On the outside is the crust. In the center is the core. The mantle is between the crust and the core.

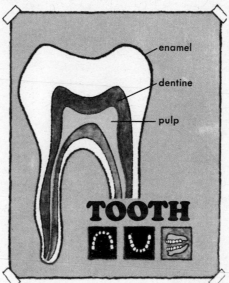

# TOOTH

enamel

dentine

pulp

## RESEARCH SKILLS

Look at the drawing of a tooth. Write the things you found out from the picture.

# CREATIVE THINKING

What do you think happened to the boy?

_____

_____

_____

_____

_____

_____

Kathleen's father and mother went to look at a house where they are going to move.
Write a question Kathleen might ask them about the house.

_____

_____

_____

_____

_____

_____

_____

_____

_____

_____

Write sentences using each
of the pictured words.

_____

_____

_____

_____

_____

_____

_____

_____

_____

_____

_____

_____

_____

_____

77

_____

Use these letters to write the names of three animals. Each name has three letters.

T T I I

D D C C

G G A A

O O P P

S S

U U O O

G G K K

D D N N

Use these letters to write the names of two animals. One name has three letters, the other five.

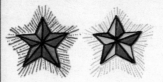

Use four letters from

# ZEBRA

to spell the name of another animal.

Write the letter you didn't use.

79

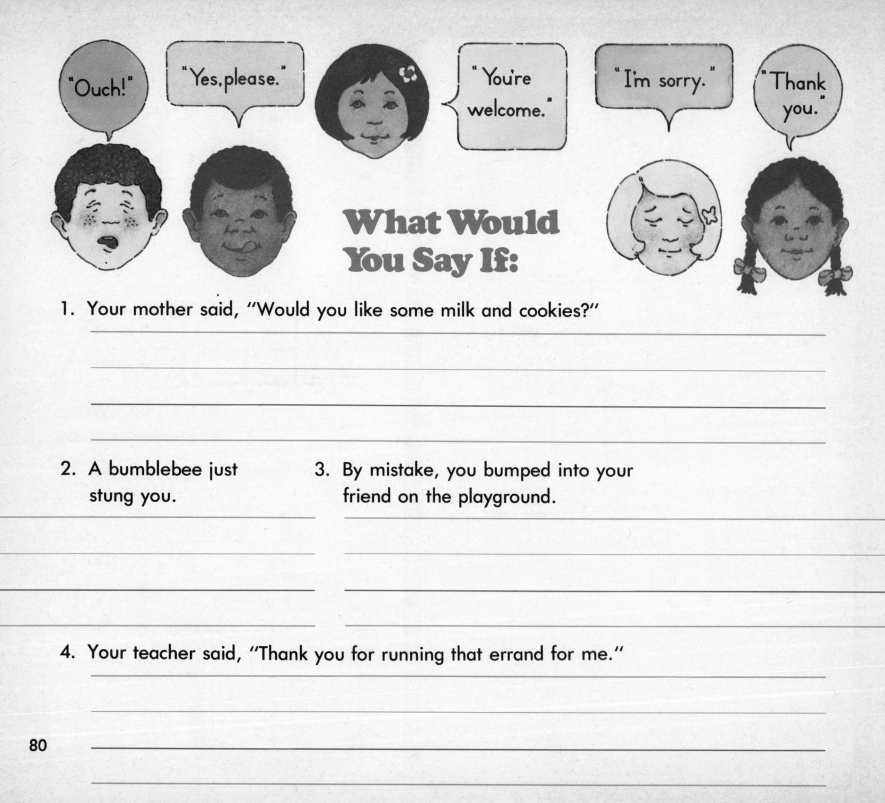

"Ouch!"

"Yes, please."

"You're welcome."

"I'm sorry."

"Thank you."

# What Would You Say If:

1. Your mother said, "Would you like some milk and cookies?"

_____

_____

_____

_____

2. A bumblebee just stung you.

3. By mistake, you bumped into your friend on the playground.

_____

_____

_____

4. Your teacher said, "Thank you for running that errand for me."

_____

_____

_____

_____

# FOLLOW THE CLUES

**1.**
What you do to a football.

_____

_____

_____

Write words with upper-case letters. Here are clues for some words you can make.

B C D E H I K O X

**2.**
Jack in the

_____

_____

_____

**3.**
Thing you sleep on

_____

_____

_____

**4.**
Short word for hello

_____

_____

_____

E

**5.**
What water is when it freezes

H

B

Upside-down is a funny town
Where folks stand on their heads.

They walk on ceilings, not on floors,
And never sleep in beds.

The children go to school at night
And stay at home by day.

They start the alphabet with Z
And end it with an A.

82

Write the two lines from page 82 that you think are the funniest.

wind butter
cow
rain book

Make **5** new
words by putting
together one word
from this circle
and one word
from this circle.

boy mill
case
bow fly

1.

2.

3.

4.

84    5.

Each picture tells what one of the children is saying. Choose a picture. On practice paper, tell what the other child is saying.

# NUMBER WORDS

The person who made this puzzle was supposed to put all these words in it.

one   two   three   four
five   six
seven   eight   nine   ten

But he forgot one of them. Read across and down to find the numbers that are written in the puzzle. Write them as you find them. Which one is missing?

1. _____

2. _____

3. _____

4. _____

5. _____

6. _____

7. _____

8. _____

9. _____

10. _____

Chris lived in a lighthouse. The lighthouse stood alone on an island. Chris's father was the lighthouse keeper. Chris was very lonely. There was nobody to play with.

One day Chris heard a little cry. It sounded like something in trouble.

Finish the story.

Write the correct answer.

"I am. I'm playing absent."
"I'm pretty when I'm clean, too."

_____

_____

_____

_____

_____

_____

_____

_____

88

**T.V. Station**

**1.**

**School**

**3.**

**2.**

**Airport 4.**

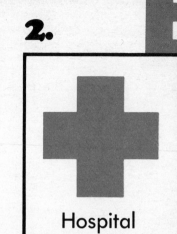

**Hospital**

Write the name of one kind of worker for each place. Use the word list to help you.

Teacher

Mechanic

Pilot

Nurse

Cameraman

Actress

Actor

Reporter

Attendant

Doctor

**1.** _____

_____

**2.** _____

_____

**3.** _____

_____

**4.** _____

89

Write a story on practice paper
about this picture.

Y Y L L

M M Q Q

**Fruits and Vegetables**

juice
potatoes
corn
green salad
tomatoes
applesauce

**Dairy Foods**

cheese
ice cream
milk
yogurt

**Protein Foods**

egg
hamburger
bacon
chicken
tuna

**Food from Grain**

cereal
bread
macaroni
cookies
biscuits

From the food lists, choose a good breakfast and dinner. Be sure that each meal has some food from each list.

 **BREAKFAST** 

 **DINNER**

_____
_____
_____
_____
_____
_____
_____
_____
_____

_____
_____
_____
_____
_____
_____
_____
_____
_____

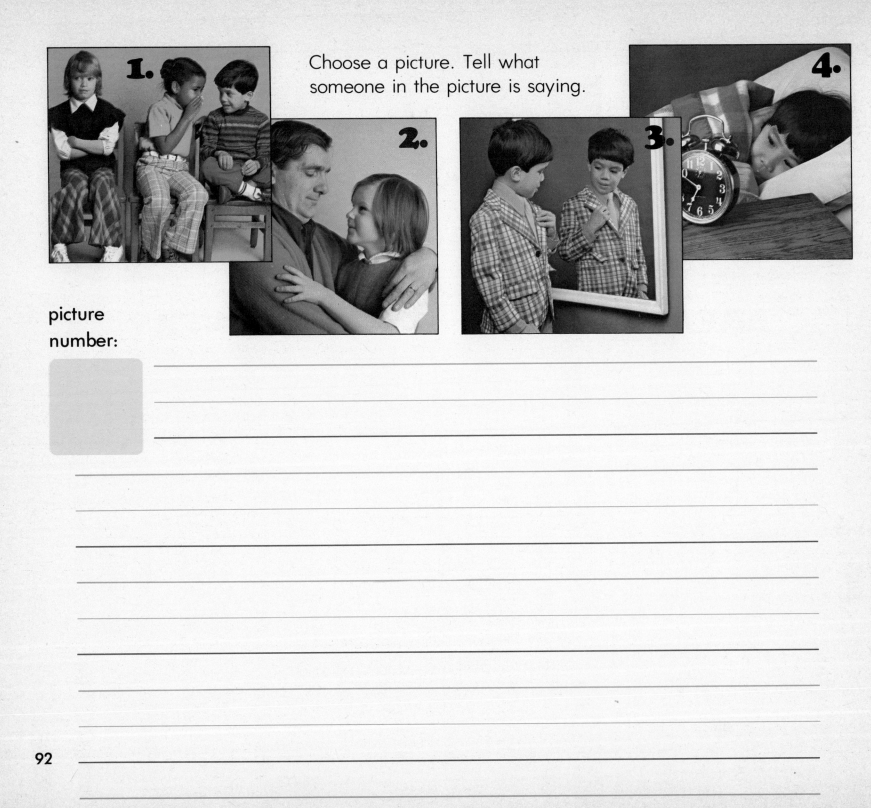

Choose a picture. Tell what someone in the picture is saying.

**1.**

**2.**

**3.**

**4.**

picture
number:

J J

F F

**1.** Who painted the window?

J

F

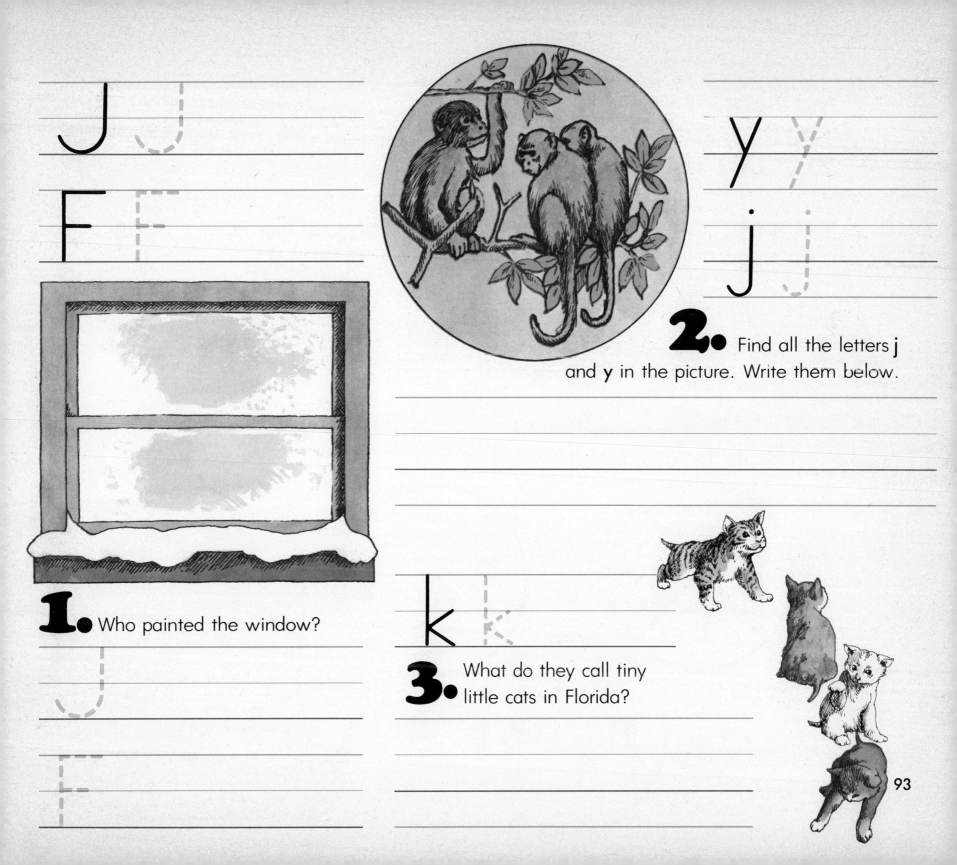

**2.** Find all the letters **j** and **y** in the picture. Write them below.

y y

j j

k k

**3.** What do they call tiny little cats in Florida?

93

# THE SPECIAL LANGUAGE OF THE LETTER X

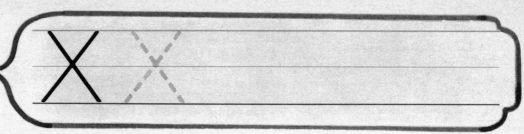

**1.** Merry Xmas

**2.** Mark where the treasure is hidden.

**3.**

# POST-TEST

_____

_____

_____

_____

_____

_____

_____

_____

## I Asked a Tiger to Tea

I asked a tiger to tea;
he said
he would come
if he could;
but he had to visit
a very old aunt
who lived in Crabapple Wood.

Write the title "I Asked a Tiger to Tea" and
then sign your name.

A B C D E F G H I

J K L M N O P Q R

S T U V W X Y Z

a b c d e f g h i j k l m

n o p q r s t u v w x y z " "

1 2 3 4 5 6 7 8 9 0 ? ! . ,